MW00387475

ISBN 1 85854 150 6

Published by Brimax Books Ltd, Newmarket, CB8 7AU England 1995.
Reprinted 1996.
Printed in China.

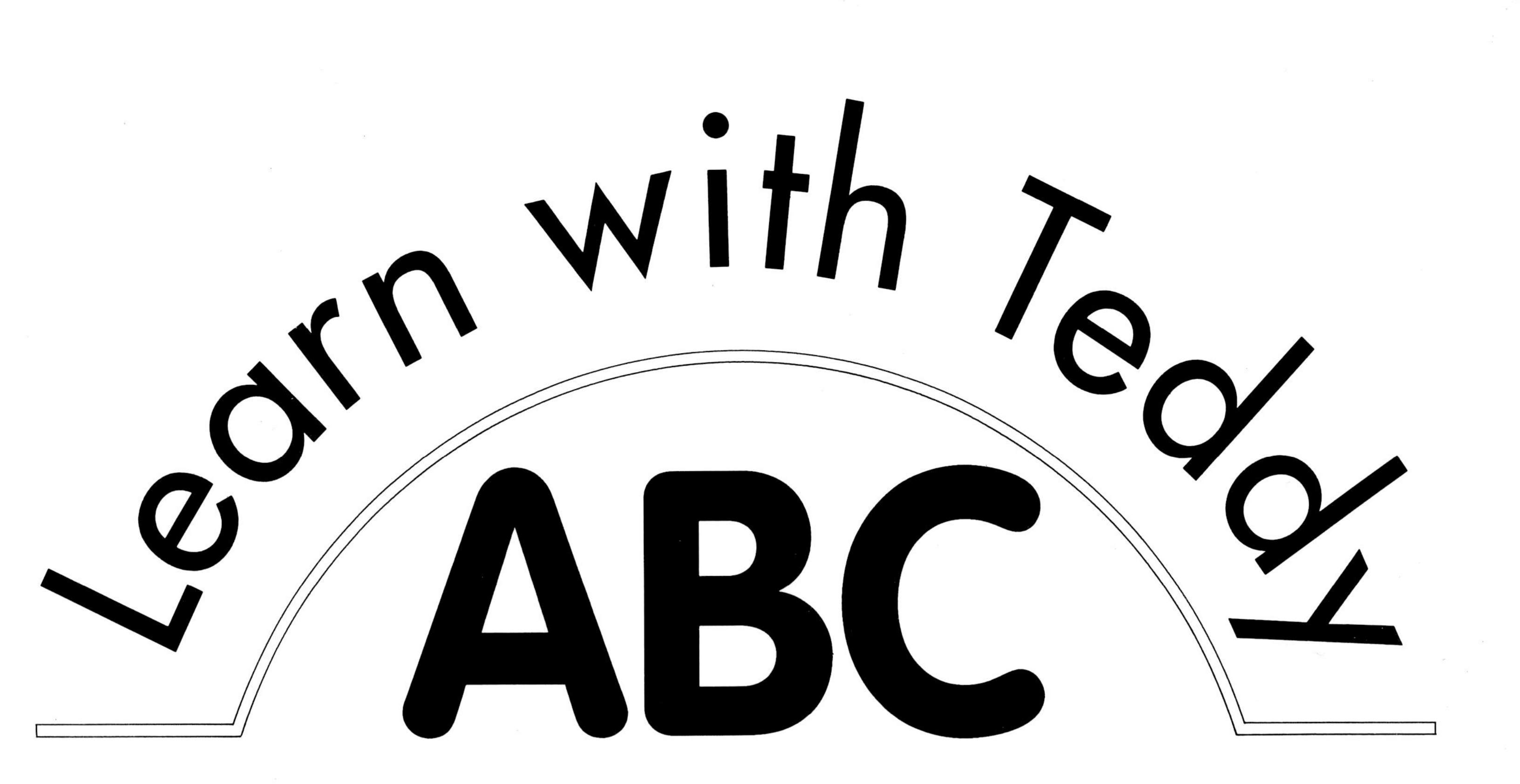

Learn with Teddy ABC

Illustrated by

Roy Trower

Brimax . Newmarket . England

a
apple
b
bib
c
cup
I give Teddy some of my apple.
First I put a bib on Teddy.
Teddy has his own cup.

I let Teddy play with my drum.
I eat an egg.

f

foot

g

goldfish

h

hat

I kick the ball with my foot.
Teddy looks at the goldfish.
Teddy wears a blue hat.

I give some ice cream to Teddy.
Look, it gets on Teddy's jeans.

I fly my kite.
Teddy plays with a lamb.
I wear red mittens.

n 

newspaper

o 

orange

p 

pillow

q 

quilt

We play a game. I am a doctor.
Teddy reads a newspaper.
I put an orange by Teddy's pillow.
I put a quilt over Teddy.

r

rabbit

s

scarf

We play with a rabbit.
Teddy's scarf keeps him warm.

t

train

u

umbrella

v

vacuum cleaner

My train is on the table.
Teddy is under the umbrella.
I am using my vacuum cleaner.

W

wheelbarrow

X

XXX

What is in the wheelbarrow?
I put XXX on top with my crayon.
That means kisses for Teddy.

y

yellow

z

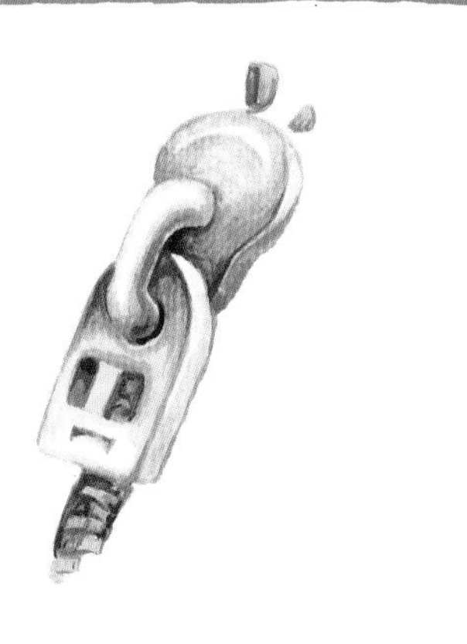

zipper

I give Teddy a yellow jacket.
It has a zipper like mine.
Teddy loves his yellow jacket.
Now Teddy looks just like me.

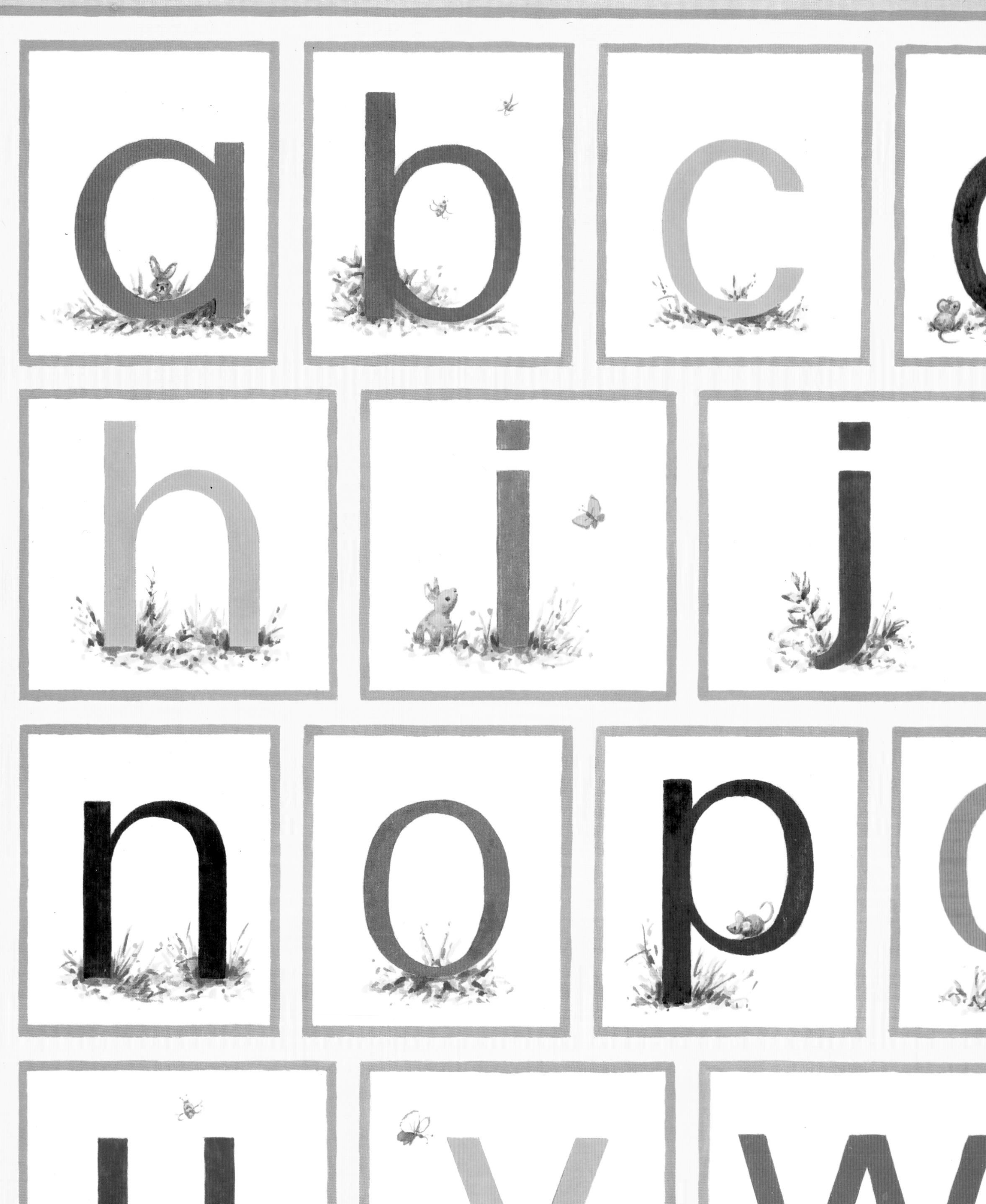
a b c
h i j
n o p

u

v

w

e
f
g
k
l
m
r
s
t
x
y
z

Old Macdonald had a Farm

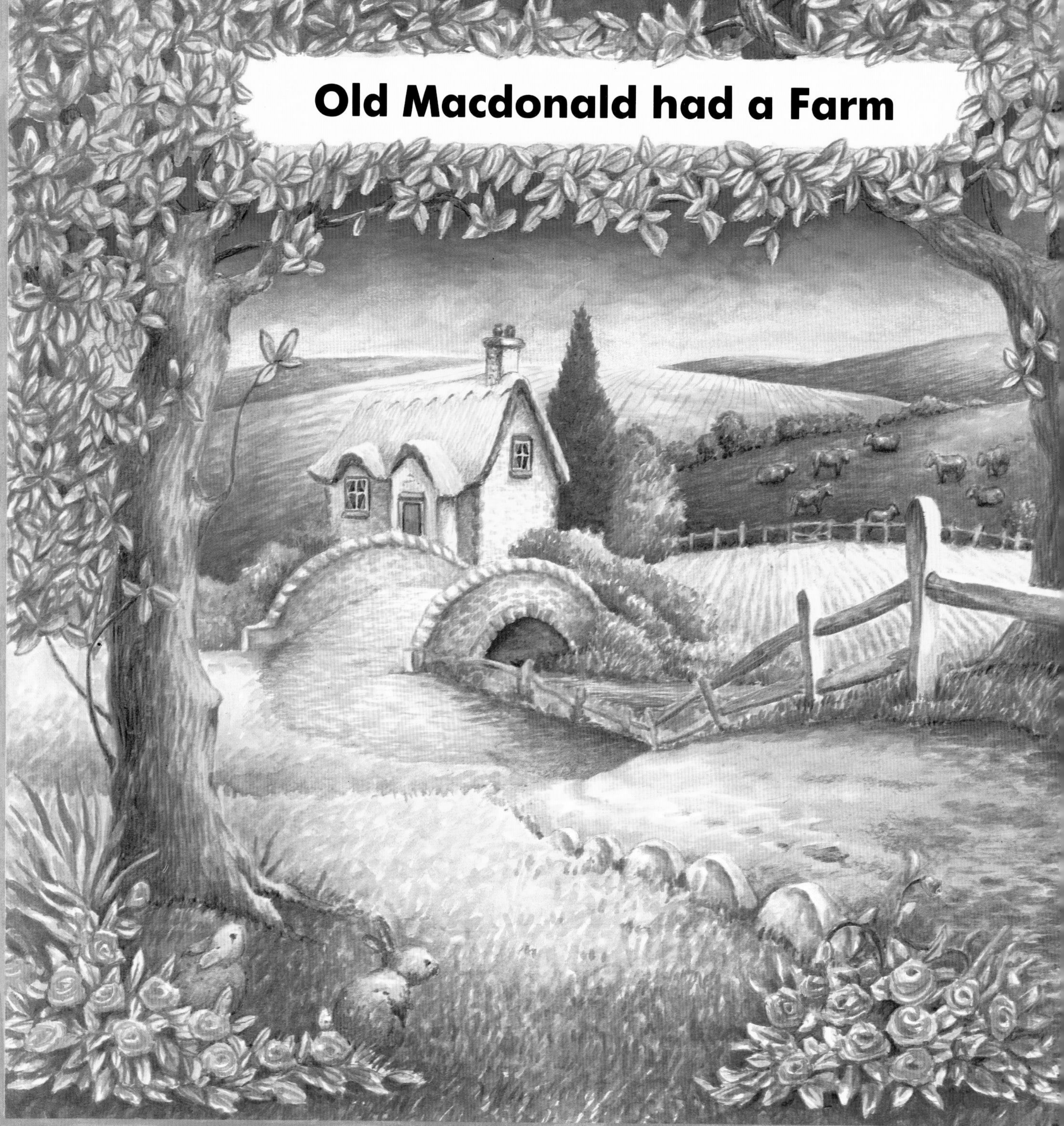

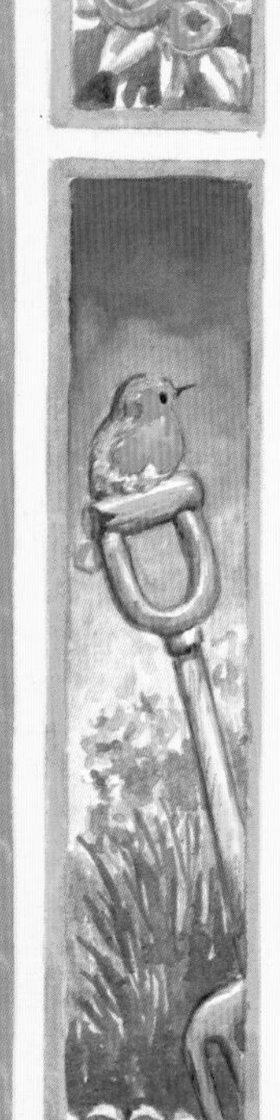

Old Macdonald had a farm,
E-i-e-i-o!
And on that farm he had a cow,
E-i-e-i-o!

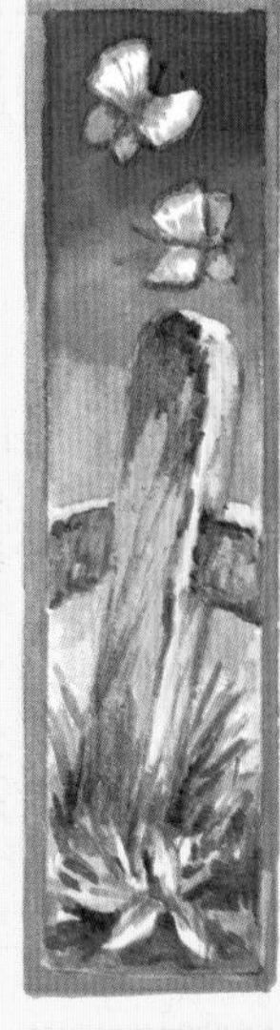

With a moo moo, here,
And a moo moo, there,
Here a moo, there a moo,
Everywhere a moo moo.
Old Macdonald had a farm,
E-i-e-i-o!

Mary had a Little Lamb

Mary had a little lamb,
Its fleece was white as snow;
And everywhere that Mary went
The lamb was sure to go.

It followed her to school one day,
That was against the rule;
It made the children laugh and play
To see a lamb at school.

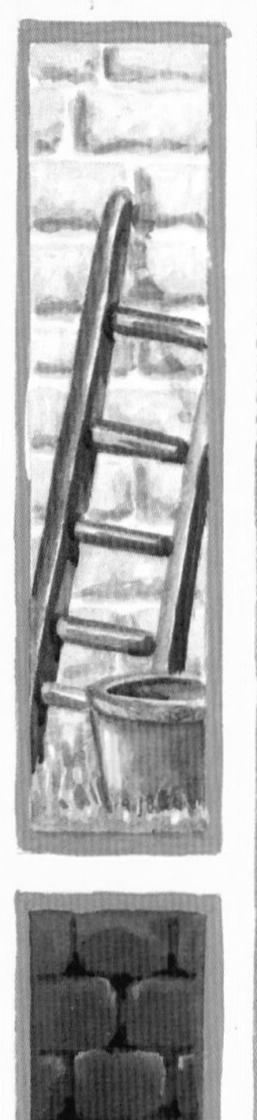

London Bridge is Falling Down

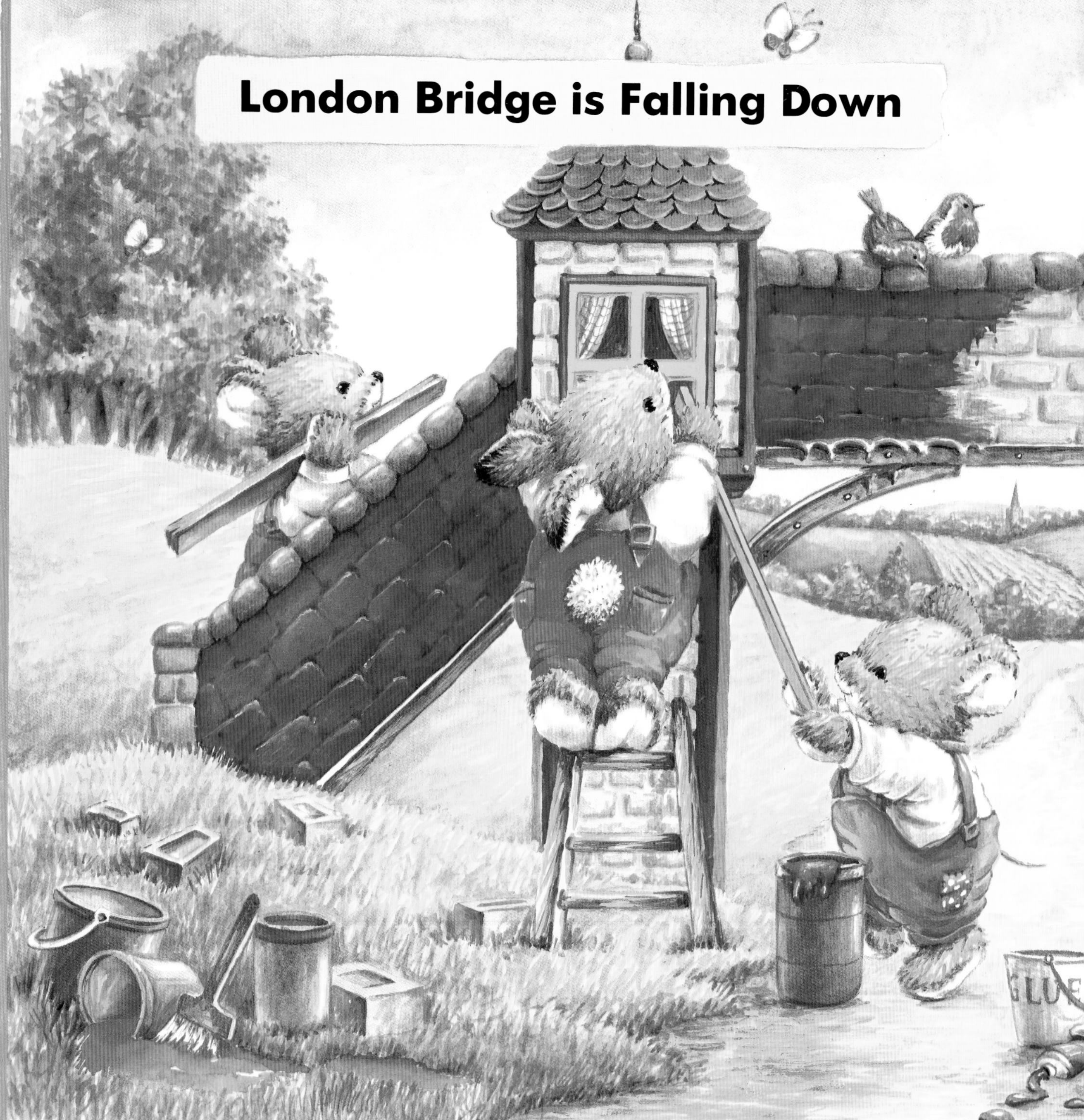

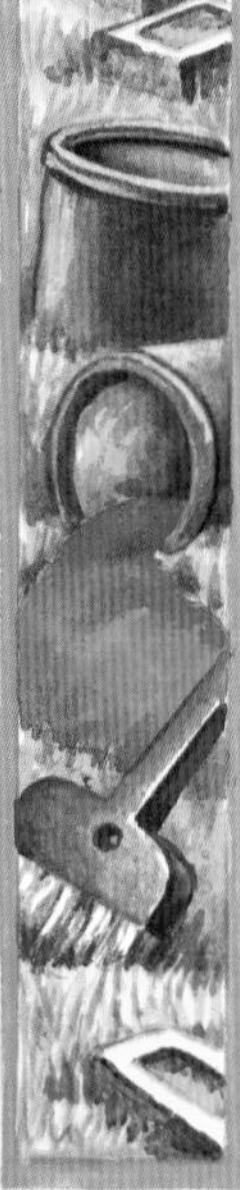

London Bridge is falling down,
Falling down, falling down,
London Bridge is falling down,
My fair lady.

Build it up with wood and clay,
Wood and clay, wood and clay,
Build it up with wood and clay,
My fair lady.

Jack and Jill

Jack and Jill went up the hill
To fetch a pail of water;
Jack fell down and broke his crown
And Jill came tumbling after.

Up Jack got and home did trot
As fast as he could caper;
He went to bed to mend his head
With vinegar and brown paper.

Hush-a-bye, Baby

Hush-a-bye, baby
On the tree top,
When the wind blows
The cradle will rock.

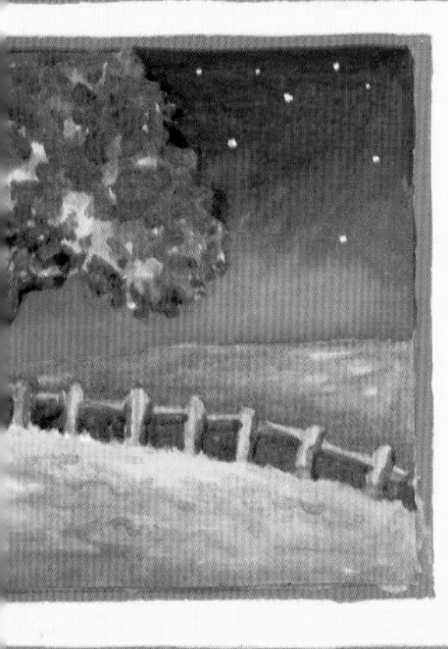

When the bough breaks
The cradle will fall,
Down will come baby,
Cradle and all.

Twinkle, Twinkle, Little Star

Twinkle, twinkle, little star,
How I wonder what you are!
Up above the world so high,
Like a diamond in the sky.

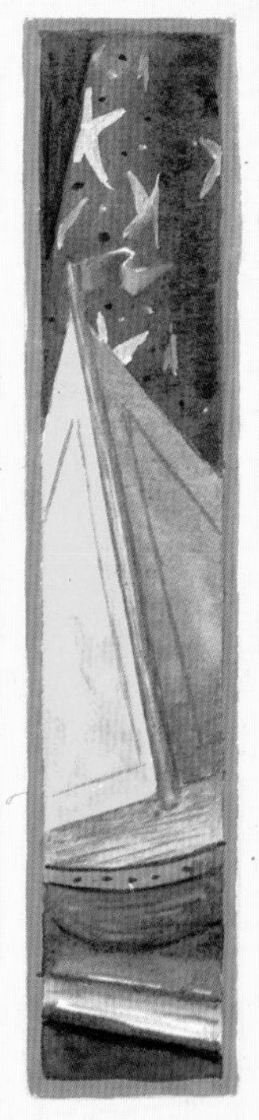

When the blazing sun is gone,
When he nothing shines upon,
Then you show your little light,
Twinkle, twinkle all the night.

1, 2 3
a b